READING 2D
PRECIOUS TREASURES
THIRD EDITION

bju press®

Greenville, South Carolina

READING 2D, Third Edition
Precious Treasures

Project Authors
Dottie Buckley
Kathleen Hynicka
Amy Schoneweis

Bible Integration
Bryan Smith

Project Editor
Debbie L. Parker

Project Coordinator
Michele White

Design Coordinator
Duane Nichols

Page Layout
Maribeth Hayes

Art Director
Elly Kalagayan

Cover & Book Designer
Andrew Fields

Permissions
Sylvia Gass
Kathleen Thompson
Carrie Walker

Illustration Coordinator
Del Thompson

Illustrators
Paula Cheadle
Cynthia Long
Sandy Mehus
Kathy Pflug
John Roberts
Benjamin Schipper
Lynda Slattery
Dana Thompson

Art Technical Consultant
John Cunningham

Photograph credits appear on page 188.

Acknowledgments:

"Until I Saw the Sea" from I FEEL THE SAME WAY by Lilian Moore. Copyright © 1967 by Lilian Moore. Used by permission of Marian Reiner. (19)

SECRET PLACE by Eve Bunting, illustrated by Ted Rand. Text copyright © 1996 by Eve Bunting. Illustrations copyright © 1996 by Ted Rand. Reprinted by permission of Clarion Books, an imprint of Houghton Mifflin Harcourt Publishing Company. All rights reserved. (30–58)

Illustrations, by John Wallner, copyright © 1989 by John Wallner; and "What Is Brown?" from HAILSTONES AND HALIBUT BONES by Mary O'Neill, text copyright © 1961 by Mary Le Duc O'Neill. Used by permission of Random House Children's Books, a division of Random House LLC (world excluding the UK and Commonwealth.) All rights reserved. Any third party use of this material, outside of this publication, is prohibited. Interested parties must apply directly to Random House LLC for permission. Also published by Egmont UK Ltd. London and used with permission (UK and Commonwealth.) (128–31)

READING 2A, 2B, 2C, and 2D, Third Edition, were originally published as READING 2A, *If Skies Be Blue*, and READING 2B, *When the Sun Rides High*, Second Edition.

Produced in cooperation with the Bob Jones University School of Education and Bob Jones Academy.

© 2015 BJU Press
Greenville, South Carolina 29614
First Edition © 1982 BJU Press
Second Edition © 1998, 2007 BJU Press

ISBN: 978-1-60682-613-3

15 14 13 12 11 10 9 8 7 6 5 4 3

CONTENTS

PRECIOUS TREASURES

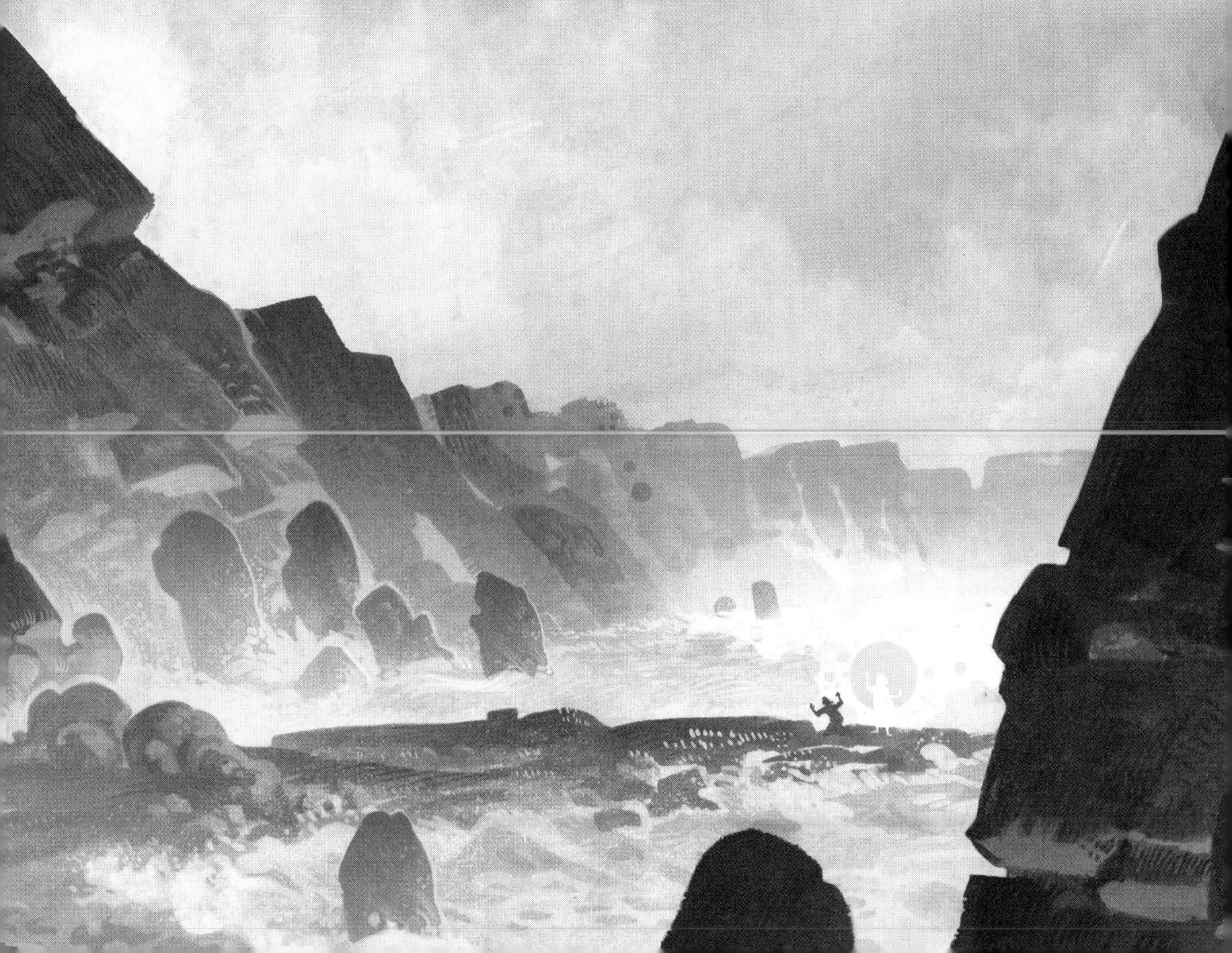

Map Reading

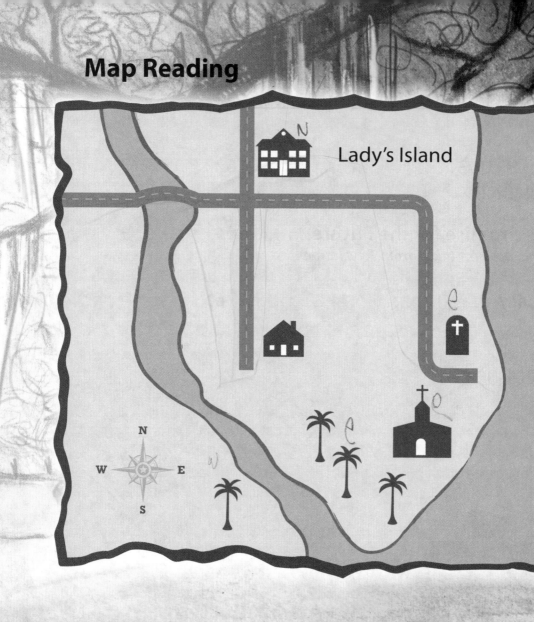

Lady's Island

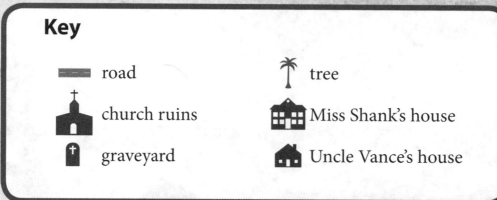

Key

- road
- church ruins
- graveyard
- tree
- Miss Shank's house
- Uncle Vance's house

2

Sea Island Mystery

A mystery by Wendy M. Harris
illustrated by Sandy Mehus

Think as You Read

What is the mystery in "Sea Island Mystery"?
How does the map help you to understand the story?

Lady's Island

"Have you looked out your window yet?" Ellie said as she stepped into Marcus's room. "Spanish moss is dripping from the branches of the trees. And can you smell the salt water?"

"Yes! Spending the summer on an island is going to be great!" said Marcus. "But I am going to miss Mom and Dad."

"I miss them already," sighed Ellie. "I hope Grandma gets better soon."

"Me too," said Marcus. He glanced out his window. "Look, there are the ponies! I can't wait to go riding."

"They look calm," said Ellie. "But I don't want to ride them."

"Not all ponies are like Sugar Foot," replied Marcus. "Come on. Aunt Fran and Uncle Vance are in the kitchen. It's time for supper."

Aunt Fran served peach pie for dessert. "Do you want anything else?" she asked as she slid another slice onto the children's plates.

"No, thank you. I'm stuffed!" said Ellie.

"May I have some more milk, please," Marcus said with a grin. "I want to know all about this island. It's so close to the ocean that there must be stories of shipwrecks and pirate treasure! Tell us everything!"

Uncle Vance laughed. "Well, there isn't much to tell. There were lots of shipwrecks off the coast. But other islands are closer to the wrecks. It's more likely that pirates chose those islands to hide their treasure. You will have to be happy with exploring Lady's Island and riding the ponies this summer."

Ellie smiled weakly at Marcus. He winked at her.

"Wait, Vance," said Aunt Fran. "What about the church mystery? Isn't there treasure in that story?"

"Tell us! Oh, please tell us!" exclaimed Marcus.

"You should visit Miss Shank," said Aunt Fran. "She knows more about the story than anyone."

"Yes, and try digging for the treasure too," said Uncle Vance. "The church burned a hundred years ago. The ruins are just a mile away. You can explore there all you want."

"Wow, a real mystery!" said Ellie.

"And what a great summer we're going to have!" said Marcus.

Lady's Island Secret

In the mornings, Marcus and Ellie fed and brushed the ponies. In the afternoons, they explored Lady's Island and the crumbled ruins of the church. They looked for the church treasure. But they did not find it.

They did find long-legged birds in the marsh and crabs that ran sideways on the beach. And with Marcus's help, Ellie started riding a gentle pony. But she would let the pony go only as fast as a walk.

After a few days, Marcus and Ellie went to see Miss Shank.

"Come on, Ellie. Let's trot. We will get there faster," said Marcus.

Ellie shook her head. "No," she said. "I like walking."

The heat of the day steamed Marcus, Ellie, and the ponies. Only a little sea breeze rippled through the Spanish moss. Ellie could feel the sweat from her pony. She sniffed. Hot pony was a nice smell.

When they got to Miss Shank's house, Marcus and Ellie tied the ponies to a tree. It was shady there. Then they walked up to the big house and knocked on the door. A lady answered. "You must be Ellie and Marcus, right? Your Aunt Fran told me I would be getting a visit from you two."

Miss Shank asked Marcus and Ellie to sit on the porch swing. Then she brought out dishes of cool banana pudding.

"Thank you!" said Marcus and Ellie together.

They had just taken a bite when Marcus asked, "What can you tell us about the missing treasure?"

"Marcus!" said Ellie.

Miss Shank laughed. "Fran told me you wanted to know about the treasure. Well, it was my great-great-great- . . . oh, I forget how many greats. But Gussie was one of those great-grandmothers. She was just a girl the night the Spanish attacked.

"Gussie heard pounding hoofs stop in front of her house. There was a pounding on the door, and she heard the door fly open.

"Gussie peeked around the corner and into the front room. Able Fuller and her father, the preacher, were quickly packing something silver into a wooden box. She heard her father telling Able to hide the treasure.

"There were silver candlesticks and offering plates and such in the box. There were some coins too. The church was not all built yet, so the preacher had been keeping these treasures in his house."

"Ooo," said Ellie.

Miss Shank went on with the story. "Gussie said she saw Able ride off with the treasure. He was headed toward the church. Soon after Able left, the Spanish soldiers searched her house. Able and the treasure were never seen again. Some people said he had run off with it."

"Did he?" asked Marcus.

"Gussie said there was never a more trusted man than Able Fuller," said Miss Shank. "Some time later Gussie heard that Able had been captured and was sent to jail in Spain. People said he was an old man before he got out. Gussie said she thought Able may have hidden the treasure before the Spanish soldiers captured him. If that's true, the treasure is still on this island."

Ellie shivered. "That story makes chills run down my back."

Marcus and Ellie said good-bye to Miss Shank and walked back to the ponies. Ellie's pony nuzzled her arm and blew its warm breath into her hand. Ellie smiled and petted its soft nose.

Marcus looked at Ellie. "We're going to find that treasure," he said.

Lady's Island Dig

"If I were Able Fuller, where would I hide treasure?" Marcus wondered as he leaned on his shovel.

Ellie sat down beside him. "We've dug all around this church! It just isn't here! I think Able did run off with the treasure," she said.

"No, he didn't, Ellie. Able was a good man. Now think! Where would you hide it?"

"All right, all right. Let's think again," sighed Ellie. She flopped onto her side, and they both thought for a while.

"Oh!" Ellie exclaimed suddenly.

"Did you think of something?" asked Marcus.

"No, I'm getting ants in my hair," said Ellie as she jumped up and shook her head.

Marcus stood and stared at all the places where they had dug. "If Spanish soldiers had come this way, they would have seen fresh dirt. They would have known that Able had been digging, and they would have found the treasure."

"Maybe they didn't see the fresh dirt," said Ellie.

"But why wouldn't they have seen it?" Marcus asked.

"Because maybe there wasn't any fresh dirt here," answered Ellie.

Marcus looked around. Across the road was a graveyard. He turned back and looked at Ellie. His eyes were opened wide. "They wouldn't think fresh dirt in a graveyard was strange! The treasure must be hidden there!"

Marcus raced across the road. Ellie was right behind him. They read names and dates from the gravestones. Marcus held his shovel as if he was ready to start digging.

"Marcus, we can't dig here!" exclaimed Ellie. "It isn't right! I won't let you!"

"I'm not going to, Ellie. Look at the dates on these gravestones. The graves aren't old enough."

"Oh, Marcus! You scared me! Let's go home."

Ellie turned back to look at the church ruins. "Marcus, wasn't the church just being built when the Spanish soldiers marched through?"

"Yes, Miss Shank said it was still being worked on. Why?" asked Marcus.

"Wouldn't there be fresh dirt around the church?" Ellie asked. "You know, from people working on the church."

"Yes," answered Marcus. "But we've dug all around the church and didn't find anything."

Ellie looked at Marcus. "But we haven't dug inside the church. What if the floor had not been put in yet?"

Marcus looked at Ellie. They both ran back across the road and into the church. They dug without saying a word. They came back every day and worked.

On the fourth day, the shovel hit something hard. Marcus and Ellie dropped to their knees and scooped dirt from around a wooden box. It looked old, very old. And it was locked.

"Oh Marcus," whispered Ellie. "Have we found it?"

"We're going to need help," replied Marcus.

"I'll go and get Uncle Vance," said Ellie.

"Ride fast," said Marcus. "I can go if you don't want to."

"No," said Ellie. "I can do it." She mounted a pony and galloped away. "I think we've found it!"

"Sea Island Mystery"

1. Where does the story take place?

2. What is the mystery in this story?

3. How does the map help you to understand the story?

4. Why do Marcus and Ellie think that the treasure is in the locked box?

Vocabulary

crumbled	offering	rippled
explore	pirate	ruins
nuzzled		

Write It

Ellie thought that she and Marcus had found the treasure. Do you think they found it? Write about it on Worktext page 263.

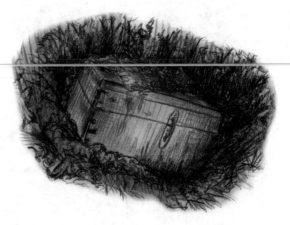

Word Pictures

When writing a poem, a poet will sometimes choose words to create a picture in our minds. He wants us to think about something in a new way.

Read the following poem.

> The seashore catches the ocean's pitch
> Then throws it back,
> Displaying captured treasure
> On its sandy track.

- What words make you think about the seashore in a different way?
- What picture does the poem make you see in your mind?

UNTIL I SAW THE SEA

Poetry by Lilian Moore
illustrated by Cynthia Long

Until I saw the sea
I did not know
that wind
could wrinkle water so.

I never knew
that sun
could splinter a whole sea of blue.

Nor
did I know before,
a sea breathes in and out
upon a shore.

High Tide, Low Tide

High tide

Low tide

TIDE POOLS

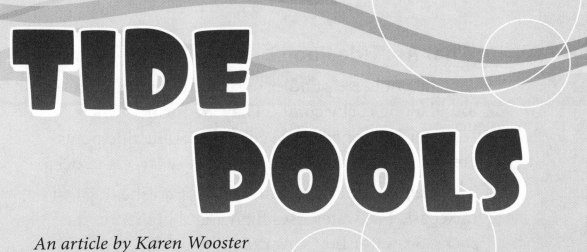

*An article by Karen Wooster
and Kathleen Hynicka*

Think as You Read

What can I learn about tide pools?

What Are Tide Pools?

Tide pools are puddles of seawater that can be found along rocky coasts. They are formed when seawater is trapped between rocks. Some tide pools are small and shallow. Others are very large and deep.

When the tide comes in, seawater crashes against the coast. The water rises higher and higher on the rocks. Seawater flows over the tide pools.

When the tide goes out, the water slowly returns to the sea. The water gets lower and lower on the rocks. Some seawater is trapped. It stays behind in the tide pools.

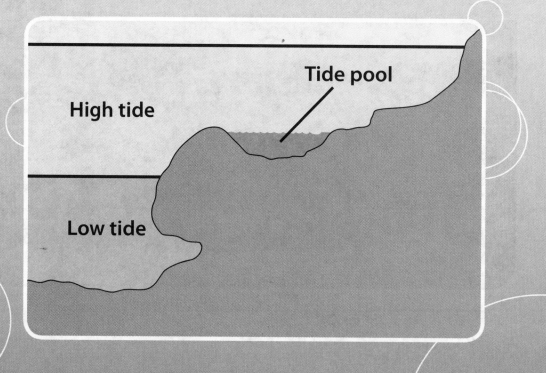

Many small animals live in the sea. When the tide comes in, there are sea animals in the water. When the tide goes out, some of the small sea animals are left behind. They make their home in the tide pool.

Sea anemone

Red sea urchin

Green sea anemone

Sea stars

Snails

Crab

A crab can swim in tide pools, but it can also run along the sand. Its eight legs are used for walking and swimming. It also has two pincers. A crab can use its pincers to pick up food and to protect itself. Its hard shell also helps to protect the crab.

Some kinds of crabs live in the empty shells left behind by other sea animals. The shell does not grow with the crab. When its shell becomes too small, the crab must find a bigger shell.

A crab has eight legs.

This hermit crab lives in a conch shell.

24

Clam

Another sea animal that can be found in tide pools is the clam. A clam lives inside a closed shell. When the clam opens its shell, it takes in seawater and tiny plants. The clam eats the tiny plants. Then it spits the seawater back out.

A clam does not swim. Usually the tide moves a clam from place to place. But a clam can also move by pushing its foot out of its shell. Then the clam can push or pull itself along rocks or sand. If there is danger, the clam can use its foot to bury itself in the sand.

A clam using its foot to move along the bottom of a tide pool

A clam using its foot to push away from its enemy

Sea Star

A sea star is also called a starfish. But a sea star is not a fish. Most sea stars have five arms. But some can have as many as 40 or 50 arms.

A sea star does not swim. It uses its arms to move slowly along the bottom of the tide pool. The bottom side of each arm has many tube feet. Each of the tube feet has a suction cup at the end. The sea star uses its tube feet to move and to cling to rocks.

If some of a sea star's arms are broken off, the sea star can grow new arms. Sometimes a sea star is broken in half. When this happens, each half can grow a new sea star.

A sea star has thousands of tube feet.

A sea star uses suction cups on its tube feet to open a clam and eat it.

Sea Urchin

A sea urchin has many spikes on its body. When danger is near, the sea urchin can hide between rocks. Its many spikes make the sea urchin look like a very prickly ball. The spikes help to protect the sea urchin from its enemies.

A red sea urchin clinging to rocks

Each sea urchin also has about 2,000 tiny tube feet. Each foot has a suction cup. When seawater rushes in and out of a tide pool, the sea urchin clings to the rocks. The sea urchin uses its tube feet to keep from being carried away by the tide.

Many other sea animals live in tide pools. They all belong to God. Some of the sea animals are big, and others are small. Some may look funny. Others are beautiful. But God has designed each of them to live in a tide pool. God cares for them all.

"Tide Pools"

1. What is a tide pool?

2. What kinds of animals live in tide pools?

3. How did the section headings and picture captions help you understand the article?

4. Are the sea animals that live in tide pools important to God? Why?

Vocabulary

cling　　　pincers　　　suction cup

Ocean Habitats

A tide pool is an **ocean habitat**. Read the pages
your teacher gives you about the ocean.

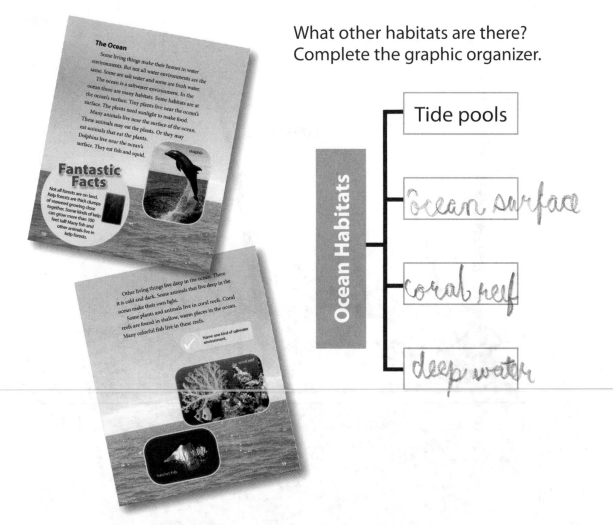

What other habitats are there?
Complete the graphic organizer.

Tide pools

Ocean surface

coral reef

deep water

Ocean Habitats

What animals could you find in other parts of
the ocean that would not be in a tide pool?

Secret Place

by EVE BUNTING • Illustrated by TED RAND

Think as You Read

Where is the secret place?

Why is the secret place special?

In the heart of the city where I live there is a secret place. Close by is a freeway where cars and trucks boom, and a railroad track with freight trains that shunt and grunt.

There are warehouses with windows blinded by dust and names paint-scrawled on their brick walls.

The lines on the telephone and electric poles web the sky. Smokestacks blow clouds to dim the sun.

But in the heart of the city where I live, low down, hidden, a river runs. The water is dark and shallow in its concrete bed. Bushes and tangled weeds cling to the slopes of the concrete walls.

Hardly anyone knows the river is here. Hardly anyone cares.

Mrs. Arren knows, and Mr. Ramirez, and Peter and Janet who are married.

I know, and my father knows, too. He works a forklift in one of the brick warehouses, and I showed him the secret place the day I found it.

The white egret found it, too.
I watch the bird float down, its
legs thin and reaching, its head
plumes fanned.

The green-winged teal knows. The buffleheads that come to water-skim know. And the circling mallards know. I've seen them here before. Peter says last year there was a mallard nest lined with feathers from the mother's breast. Later there were ducklings. "They'll nest here again," Peter says. I jump up and down. "Ducklings! Perfect!"

sparrows

mallard.

Mrs. Arren and Mr. Ramirez and Janet and Peter bring binoculars. They let me look through them. The sparrows lined up on the barbed wire fence seem big as mud hens.

Peter tells me the names of the birds. He is like a bird himself, with hair the color of a cinnamon teal.

bufflehead.

coot

cinnamon teal

green-winged teal

43

In the heart of the city where I live there is always noise: The growl of traffic, the snort of trains, the *beep-beep* of a backing truck.

The secret place has its own noise: The cackle of coots, the quack of teals, the *rah-rah* of the mallards that ring the sky.

Peter and Janet brought me here one night. We stood while behind us the city jangled.

The secret place was at peace. The birds had nested, the river ran, slow as syrup. Tucked together, the ducks slept.

A coyote came to lap the shadowed water.
A possum carried her children to drink.

"How did they find this place?"
I asked. "They have always been
here," Janet said. "Before the city
grew there was wilderness. This
is all that's left. Wild things need
quiet. We do, too."

The phone wires rocked the moon
in their cradle of lines. The stars
rested bright on the telephone poles.

"I want to tell everyone what's here," I said. "Be careful," Peter said. "Some people might want to take the secret place and change it."

"I'd never want that to happen," I said. "I told my father, but he is good with secrets. I will be careful who else I tell."

I will only say that close to a freeway and a railroad track and tall smoking chimneys, in the heart of the city where I live there is a secret place.

If you can find it, there
may be ducklings.

Secret Place

1. Where is the secret place?

2. Look back in the story. What picture words does the author use to describe the city? What words does she use to describe the secret place?

3. Do you think the secret place is special? Why?

4. Where do you live? Is it like the noisy city, or is it like the quiet secret place?

5. The Bible says that Jesus went alone to a quiet place where He could pray. Why do you think that Jesus chose a quiet place?

Vocabulary

barbed wire	freeway	traffic
concrete	jangled	warehouses
forklift	syrup	wilderness

Planning a Book

Eve Bunting is the author of *Secret Place.* The story tells of a boy who lives in the city. The boy finds a quiet secret place that is very different from the busy city.

When Mrs. Bunting planned this story, she might have used a T-chart like the one below.

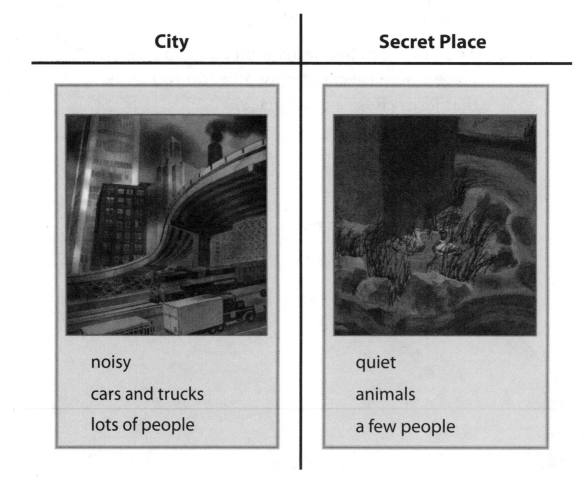

City	Secret Place
noisy	quiet
cars and trucks	animals
lots of people	a few people

1. Do you have a special place that you like to visit?

2. What makes the place special?

3. How is your special place different from the place where you live?

Use the chart on Worktext page 279 to plan a story about your special place.

Where I Live	My Special Place

Reading Songs

Verses of a song or hymn are called **stanzas**. To sing the first stanza, sing the words in line number 1. To sing the second stanza, sing the words in line number 2.

The author of the words

The composer of the music

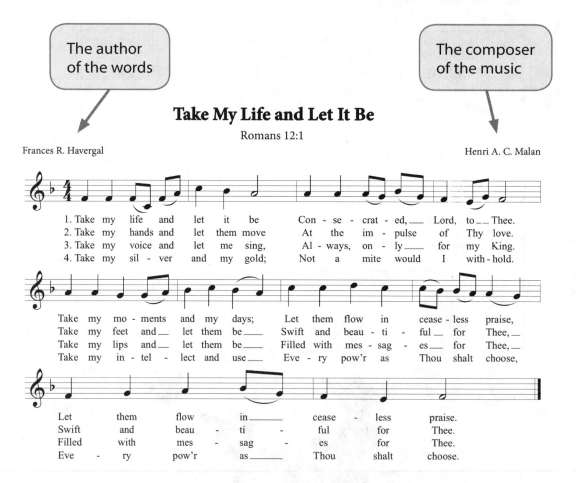

Take My Life and Let It Be

Romans 12:1

Frances R. Havergal

Henri A. C. Malan

1. Take my life and let it be   Con - se - crat - ed, ___ Lord, to ___ Thee.
2. Take my hands and let them move   At the im - pulse of Thy love.
3. Take my voice and let me sing,   Al - ways, on - ly ___ for my King.
4. Take my sil - ver and my gold;   Not a mite would I with - hold.

Take my mo - ments and my days;   Let them flow in cease - less praise,
Take my feet and ___ let them be ___   Swift and beau - ti - ful ___ for Thee, ___
Take my lips and ___ let them be ___   Filled with mes - sag - es ___ for Thee, ___
Take my in - tel - lect and use ___   Eve - ry pow'r as Thou shalt choose,

Let them flow in ___ cease - less praise.
Swift and beau - ti - ful for Thee.
Filled with mes - sag - es for Thee.
Eve - ry pow'r as ___ Thou shalt choose.

Let Me Sing

Frances Havergal
December 14, 1836–June 3, 1879

Biography by Eileen M. Berry
illustrated by Paula Cheadle

Think as You Read

Why did Frances write the hymn "Take My Life and Let It Be"?

Little Caged Bird

"Catch me if you can!" Frances held her skirt up away from her skates. Then she glided off across the pond, laughing.

Ellen sighed as she skated slowly toward her younger sister. "Frances! It's time to go home. You still have schoolwork to do."

Frances's giggles rang out over the ice. "All right, I'm coming," she said. As Frances turned back toward the house, she saw her father standing at the edge of the pond.

"Come home, girls," he called. "I have something to tell you."

Frances stopped laughing when she saw the sober look on Papa's face. She slid across the ice, climbed up on the bank, and pulled off her skates. "Is it bad news, Papa?"

Papa ruffled Frances's blond curls. "Not all bad," he said. "Wait and see."

Frances and her brother and sisters gathered beside the warm fireplace. Mother was sitting in the armchair, wrapped in a blanket.

Papa cleared his throat. "I have been offered a new job," he said. "There is a church in Worcester that needs a preacher. We've been happy in our country churches, but city churches need preachers too. Mother and I have prayed about this need. We believe God wants us to move to Worcester."

Frances was very still. She looked down at her hands, still holding her skates. No more skating on icy ponds. No more picking flowers in open fields. No more walks in the woods to hear the birds' songs. Moving to the city would take her away from all these things she loved.

Later Frances curled up on her bed with her doll. Tears ran down her cheeks and made a wet spot on her pillow. Why would God let this happen?

After moving to Worcester, Frances tried to be happy. She knew Papa liked his new church. She did her schoolwork. She laughed and joked. She teased her brother and sisters. But sometimes she still missed the country.

One day Papa found Frances in her small room staring out at the sunset. "Poor child," he said. "You are like a little caged bird here. Can you learn to praise God, even in this place?"

Over the next two years, Mother became very sick. Frances wrote poems and little songs. She sang her songs at Mother's bedside.

One day Mother reached out and took Frances's hand. "My dear," she said softly, "you are my youngest girl. I worry about you sometimes. God has a plan for you. Pray that He will help you to learn all He wants you to learn. And that He will give you a love for what He has planned."

Mother gently pulled Frances closer and looked right into her eyes. "Remember, nothing but the precious blood of Christ can make you clean in His sight."

Soon afterward Mother died. There were days when Frances could not sing. She often stood at the window and looked up at the clouds. Were all those things her parents believed about God true? Was He really loving? Was He really good?

69

When Frances was fourteen, she went to boarding school. Her teachers taught her the Bible just as her parents had. Frances read her Bible alone in her room every day. Sometimes she thought of Mother's words. *Nothing but the precious blood of Christ can make you clean . . .* But Frances kept her questions about God locked up in her heart.

One day a kind woman spoke with Frances. "You know God's promises, Frances. You know Jesus loves you. You know He died and rose for you. Couldn't you trust Him?"

The question echoed in Frances's mind the rest of the day. She sat at her window that afternoon. A bird was hopping about on the lawn, plucking up seeds from the ground. "Yes, Jesus," Frances whispered. "I can trust you, and I will. I will give my life to you."

The Songbird Flies

Trusting Jesus as her Savior changed Frances. She knew that all she had been taught about God was true. She knew that God loved her. And she knew that God was always good.

It was as if the little caged bird had spread her wings to fly. Frances knew that her mother was right. God had a special plan for her life. She worked hard at school. And her teachers could see that God had given Frances special gifts. She learned a number of languages. And she knew many books of the Bible by heart.

When Frances grew up, she was often asked to sing in public. She also began to publish her poems and hymns. But Frances's health was not good, and she had to stop singing.

One day she told a friend, "I think singing made me love the praise of my friends more than I loved God. I asked Him to take away my singing if it was keeping me from loving Him most of all. Now He has taken away that gift. I thank Him for hearing my prayer."

Frances could not sing in public anymore, but she kept writing hymns. For the rest of her life she wrote about things God had taught her. One hymn she wrote is about Jesus' blood that had made her clean. When Frances wrote this hymn, she might have been thinking about what her mother had said. "Remember, nothing but the precious blood of Christ can make you clean in His sight."

Precious, precious blood of Jesus,
Shed on Calvary;
Shed for rebels, shed for sinners,
Shed for me.

Though thy sins are red like crimson,
Deep in scarlet glow,
Jesus' precious blood can make them
White as snow.

One of Frances's best-known hymns tells of giving herself to God. In "Take My Life and Let It Be," Frances names many of the gifts God had given to her. She could give these gifts back to Him. She could use them to serve Him and to tell others about Him.

Take my feet, and let them be
Swift and beautiful for Thee.

Take my voice, and let me sing
Always, only for my King.

Take my lips, and let them be
Filled with messages for Thee.

Frances wanted her life, her gifts, and all that she owned to be God's. One day she thought about some of the words that she had written.

Take my silver and my gold,
Not a mite would I withhold.

Frances lifted the lid of her large wooden jewelry case. She looked at the sparkling jewelry inside. "If I really meant those words," she thought, "I cannot keep anything from God. This is another little step I can take."

One by one she wrapped up the pieces of jewelry. Then she packed them to be sold. The money would go to help the Lord's work. "I never packed a box with such joy," Frances wrote later.

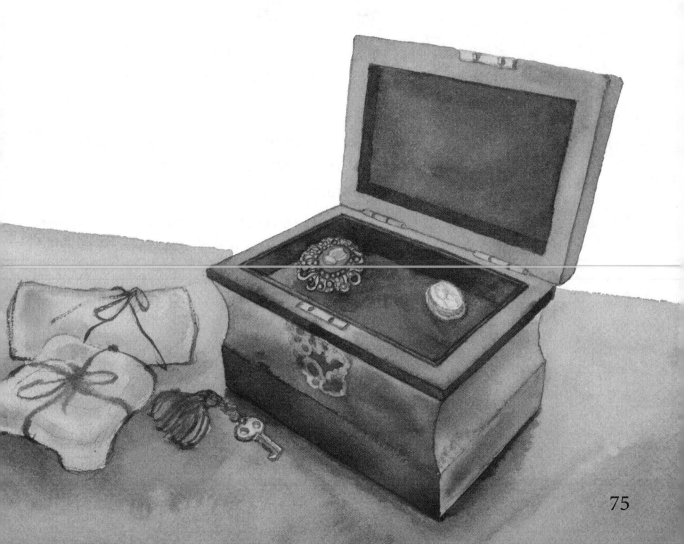

Frances loved to see new places. She traveled as much as she could when she felt well. Once while traveling, she caught a cold. She became so sick that her doctor thought she might die. Frances had perfect peace about living or dying. She knew that whatever God wanted for her was best. She did get well, and later that year Frances wrote these words.

Stayed upon Jehovah, hearts are fully blest,
Finding, as He promised, perfect peace and rest.

Frances Havergal lived to be only forty-three years old. During her life, she had written many hymns. Her hymns are still sung in churches around the world.

The little girl who learned to trust God trusted Him to the end. After her death, the words to one of Frances's hymns were found in her Bible.

I am trusting Thee, Lord Jesus!
Never let me fall!
I am trusting Thee, forever,
And for all.

"Let Me Sing"

1. Why did Frances write "Take My Life and Let It Be"?

2. Frances wrote, "Take my silver and my gold, Not a mite would I withhold." How did she show that these words were true in her life?

3. Do you think that "Let Me Sing" is a good title for the story? Why?

4. Frances learned to do the things that showed her love for God. What are things that you do to show your love for God?

Vocabulary

boarding school	languages	publish
caged	precious	sober

CAPTAIN STRIPE'S GOLD

Fantasy by Milly Howard
illustrated by Dana Thompson

Think as You Read

What is Captain Stripe's gold?

The Trail

Zack Zebra trotted to the far end of the plain. He tossed his head and looked back as the other zebras gathered around Captain Stripe.

Zack laughed at Captain Stripe's words. "Stay out of the jungle!" Zack said to himself. "I get so tired of Captain Stripe's orders! Just because he's the new leader, he thinks he knows everything."

Captain Stripe's father had once been the leader of the zebras and had taught his son well. No one had been surprised when Stripe became the new leader.

Captain Stripe doesn't have a son, Zack thought. I will be the next leader of the zebras. Then I will do whatever I want.

"I'm thirsty," Zack said to himself. He looked at the trail leading into the jungle. Then he looked back at the muddy stream where the zebras were drinking. "That water is too muddy to drink," he said as he trotted into the jungle. Branches hung over the trail, shutting out the bright sunlight.

Crack! Snap! Zack slowed his steps, quickly looking from side to side. He suddenly stopped as a huge head appeared between some branches. He stared at the two big eyes and the long trunk. He had never been this close to such a large elephant.

"Wh-who are you?" asked Zack.

"I am Mumba," boomed the elephant. "Where are you going?"

"I'm g-g-going to get something to drink," Zack replied. He didn't want to say any more, so he galloped away.

Mumba stood still and watched Zack until the trees hid him from sight.

As Zack headed farther into the jungle, more and more vines and ferns crowded the trail. Zack had to slow down to avoid some of the tangled vines. At last he heard the sound of flowing water.

"Water!" he shouted, running toward the sound. Zack stopped at the edge of a river. As he bent to drink, a voice said, "*Psst!*" Startled, Zack looked up. But there was no one to be seen. He bent to drink again.

"You aren't very fffriendly, are you?" the voice asked. Zack leaped back as a large vine dropped down beside him. Two yellow eyes gazed into his.

"How about thisss, Croc?" the vine hissed. "Here's a ssstriped horsssse that cannot talk."

Just then Zack saw what seemed to be a log in the water. It was floating toward his legs. Then it opened its eyes and looked at Zack sleepily.

"Cannot talk? What kind of beast is it?" the log asked. Then it yawned, showing rows of sharp, pointed teeth.

Logs and vines that talk! Zack turned around quickly.

Gold!

"Don't run away," the voice called. "We won't hurt you. I'm Mona, the python," the voice went on. "Thisss is my friend Croc. We don't get many visssitorsss down here, do we, Croc?"

The crocodile sank a little lower in the water. "Not often enough anyway," he muttered with a hungry look in his eyes.

Croc looked at the zebra. "What are you doing in this part of the jungle?" he asked.

"I needed a drink," answered Zack, tossing his head. "I'm very thirsty."

"By all meansss drink as much as you like," Mona said. She coiled up around another branch.

Zack stretched his neck carefully to drink from the river. "This river is nice," he said. "We just have shallow brooks to drink from back on the plains. The water is often muddy from so many animals walking in it. Why do you two have this river all to yourselves?" he asked.

"Well," Mona said. She paused and glanced slyly at Croc. "There are ssso many riversss here that everyone has hisss own watering place."

"Really?" asked Zack. "Why, this part of the jungle would be just the place for our herd. Captain Stripe is always looking for new watering places. I wonder why he doesn't bring us here."

The crocodile rolled his eyes at Mona. "Maybe Captain Stripe doesn't want you to know about the gold," he replied.

"Gold? Real gold?" asked Zack.

Mona swayed back and forth. "Oh, I thought everyone knew about the gold. Robbersss hid it in a shady place many yearsss ago. Now the vinesss have grown ssso thick that they have hidden the gold from sssight. But I know where it isss." Her eyes glowed.

"What we need is a nice, strong fellow like you to fetch it for us," said Croc. "If you help us, we will gladly share the gold with you."

Zack looked at Croc, and then he looked at Mona. There was something about the two of them that bothered him. Zack seemed to hear Captain Stripe's words warning him to stay out of the jungle. But he shook his head and put the voice out of his mind.

"Where is the gold?" Zack asked. "I'll help you get it. Then I can take real gold to the zebras. They will not think Captain Stripe's words are so good then! And I will not have to wait until I am older to be the leader!"

"The gold is on the other ssside of the river," said Mona. "You must crosss the bridge."

Zack looked at the old wooden bridge swaying back and forth over the river. "I do not think . . ." he began.

"Are you really afraid?" asked Mona, laughing. "A leader cannot be afraid. It'sss just a short trip. Sssoon you'll be back with the gold."

The crocodile winked at Mona. "Bigger beasts than you have used the bridge," he said.

Real Gold

Zack put one hoof on the bridge, then another one. The boards creaked under him as he moved. He stepped slowly and carefully. Suddenly, there was no board for the next step. And it was a long way to the next board.

Zack looked down at the water and saw the hooded eyes of the crocodile looking up at him. Croc's eyes did not look friendly. Something about Croc and Mona still worried him.

"Come on! It's not far now. You can easily jump to the next board." Croc blinked his yellow eyes and brushed his tongue across his mouth.

Zack did not move. He thought, Why does hardly anyone come to visit Mona and Croc? This is a peaceful place, and the water is good. Surely the few visitors would have told others about the river. Then Zack had a horrible thought. What if none of the visitors were ever able to leave?

Zack carefully turned and leaped off the sagging bridge. The empty bridge swayed back and forth. Suddenly it broke with a loud snap! It splashed into the water. The crocodile's mouth sprang shut on a board.

"Ouch!" groaned Croc, sinking into the water.

Just as Zack turned to leave, Mona dropped on him. He kicked and kicked, but she only coiled around him more tightly. He could not free himself from her grasp.

Oh, Captain Stripe, Zack thought, your words are better than real gold! I wish I had listened to you!

"Stop!" a voice boomed. The voice sounded like thunder as it rang through the jungle. Zack looked up at Mumba, the huge elephant he had seen by the trail.

"Go away," hissed Mona.

"Let him go," Mumba ordered. "I could crush the likes of you with only one of my feet."

Mumba lifted one foot. Mona slowly released the frightened zebra. She glared at the elephant and slithered away. "There will be another time," Mona said. Then she was gone.

Mumba turned to Zack. "Is this where you came to drink? I thought Captain Stripe kept all of you zebras on the plains. He knows that there you are safe from Mona and Croc."

Zack hung his head, feeling ashamed. "He does, but I thought I was wiser than Captain Stripe. Now I know why he is the captain of the zebras and I am not."

Mumba shook his head. "Captain Stripe wants to protect you. He is a wise leader because he thinks of your safety."

"I know that now," Zack replied. "I see why the other zebras listen to Captain Stripe's words as if they were gold. His words were much better than real gold today."

"How much better is it to get wisdom than gold! and to get understanding rather to be chosen than silver!"

Proverbs 16:16

"Captain Stripe's Gold"

1. What was Captain Stripe's gold?

2. Why did Zack say that Captain Stripe's words were like gold?

3. Why did Mona and Croc say that there was gold in the jungle?

4. Were Mona and Croc's words valuable? Why?

5. Read again Proverbs 16:16 at the end of the story. Since all wisdom comes from God, whose words are always much better than gold?

Vocabulary

avoid	herd	plain
coiled	horrible	sleepily
ferns		

Read as a Play

Mona

Narrator

Croc

Zack

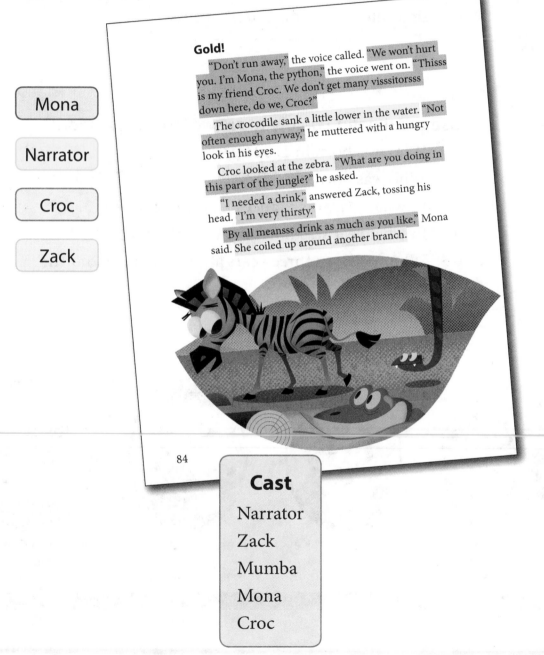

Gold!

"Don't run away," the voice called. "We won't hurt you. I'm Mona, the python," the voice went on. "Thisss is my friend Croc. We don't get many visssitorsss down here, do we, Croc?"

The crocodile sank a little lower in the water. "Not often enough anyway," he muttered with a hungry look in his eyes.

Croc looked at the zebra. "What are you doing in this part of the jungle?" he asked.

"I needed a drink," answered Zack, tossing his head. "I'm very thirsty."

"By all meansss drink as much as you like," Mona said. She coiled up around another branch.

84

Cast

Narrator
Zack
Mumba
Mona
Croc

When Were They Born?

A **timeline** shows important events.

Use the timeline below to answer these questions.

1. Who was born in 1752?
2. Who was born in 1871?
3. In what year was Frances Havergal born?
4. In what year was Jonathan Goforth born?
5. Who was born three years after Jonathan Goforth?

Betsy Ross born	Francis Scott Key born	Frances Havergal born	Jonathan Goforth born
1752	1779	1836	1859

JONATHAN'S
TREASURE

*Historical fiction by Milly Howard and Susan W. Young
illustrated by John Roberts*

Think as You Read

What is Jonathan's treasure?

Billy Sunday
born

Wilbur Wright
born

Orville Wright
born

1862   1867   1871   2000

Five Cents

Jonathan Goforth was born on his family's farm in Canada in 1859. He had nine brothers and one sister. As they grew up, the Goforth children learned to work on the farm.

Those were difficult times for everyone in Canada. Many farm owners had no money to hire men to do farm work. All of the Goforth children worked hard to help their family.

When Jonathan was a young boy, a lady came to visit his family.

"Would you like to see my chickens?" Jonathan asked.

"That would be very nice," the visitor replied.

After dinner Jonathan took her to the chicken house and showed her the chickens.

Soon it was time for the visitor to leave. She climbed onto the seat of her buggy. Then just before the buggy rolled out of the yard, she gave Jonathan five pennies.

What a surprise! Jonathan had never before had five cents of his own.

"Mother!" Jonathan called as he ran up the porch steps, holding the five cents tightly. "The lady gave me five pennies! May I go to the candy store?"

"No, Jonathan," his mother answered. "You cannot go today."

Jonathan looked up at his mother. "Please," he begged.

"Jonathan, look." Mother gently turned Jonathan toward the road. The sky over the dark trees was pink.

"I see, Mother," he sighed. "It will soon be dark. But I can go first thing in the morning! I'll get up before daylight and do my chores!" he added.

"Not in the morning, Jonathan. Tomorrow is the Lord's Day," Mother reminded him. "You will have to wait until next week to spend your five cents." She gave him a hug and went inside the house.

Jonathan sat down on the steps and leaned sadly against the post. He did not see the sky turn from pink to red. He did not hear the wind in the trees. All he could see in his mind was the candy store. He reached into his pocket and felt the five cents.

The Battle

In his mind Jonathan walked down the street to the candy store. He could hear the bell jingle as he opened the door and walked inside. He could feel the pine boards under his bare feet. He could see the jars and jars of candy. There were lemon drops, orange suckers, peppermint sticks—almost everything a boy could wish for. For five cents he could get six sticks of candy!

"Let me see," Jonathan thought. "I'll start with the peppermint sticks, and then . . ."

Suddenly, Jonathan sat up straight. An offering was going to be taken the next day at Sunday school. It was to help send missionaries to faraway lands to preach the gospel.

"I should give my five pennies to the missionaries," he thought. "But the lady gave me the money to do what I wanted with it. And I want to buy some candy. Oh, why did I have to remember the offering now?"

Jonathan thought about the missionaries. Then he thought about the candy. He did not know much about missionaries, but he knew all about candy. He started choosing his candy again.

"I'll start with the peppermint sticks, and then . . ." But it was no use. Jonathan could not stop thinking about the offering. "How could five cents help the missionaries to tell others about Christ?" he thought. "It isn't very much."

That night Jonathan put his five pennies on the table beside his bed. Mother came to his room to tuck him in.

"Have you prayed yet, Jonathan?" Mother asked.

"No, Mother," Jonathan sighed. "I do not feel like praying tonight."

"What's wrong?" she asked.

Jonathan just shrugged.

"Are you angry?" asked Mother.

Jonathan shook his head.

"It's best to take care of whatever is bothering you before you go to sleep," Mother said gently. "Talk to God about it, Jonathan."

After Mother left, Jonathan tried three times to pray. But the most he could say was, "Dear Lord . . ."

Jonathan tossed and turned in his bed. His heart was hurting. He thought about the missionaries and the pennies. He thought about the candy and the people who needed to hear about Christ. He could not sleep. He thought and thought.

After a long time, Jonathan decided to give the pennies to the missionaries. At last he was able to pray. Then he smiled and fell asleep.

The Offering Basket

The next morning, the sunshine woke Jonathan. He jumped out of bed and ran to the window. The milk pails rattled as his brothers did their chores in the barn. He dressed quickly and ran to join them. He had to hurry to finish his chores.

He was the last one to slide into his place at the table.

"You're a little late today," Father said.

"Yes, sir. I slept late," Jonathan said.

As Jonathan was dressing for church, he saw the five pennies on the bedside table. He picked them up to put them in his pocket. He wanted to give the pennies to the missionaries, but he began to think about the candy again. He could almost taste the candy he wanted.

"Jonathan!" called his father.

Jonathan stuffed the pennies into his pocket as he ran outside. His brothers grabbed Jonathan's arms and lifted him into the wagon. Then the wagon pulled away from the house and headed toward the church. Jonathan held on tightly to keep from falling out. His family chattered happily, but Jonathan kept silent. He was thinking.

When they arrived at church, Jonathan was the last one to get out of the wagon. He waited until the rest of his brothers walked inside. Then he went in behind them.

While everyone else sang, Jonathan thought some more about the pennies. He thought and thought. Then he knew what he would do.

The time came to pass the offering basket.

Jonathan could hear *clink* after *clink* as people dropped in their offerings. When the basket reached his bench, he watched it pass from brother to brother. Everyone had something to give. When the basket reached Jonathan, he opened his hand and dropped in the five pennies.

Jonathan grinned as he passed the offering basket. He felt happier than if he had a whole store full of candy! His heart was not hurting anymore.

"Jonathan's Treasure"

1. What was Jonathan's treasure?

2. Why do you think the second part of the story was called "The Battle"?

3. Is it wrong to buy candy with your money? Why?

4. Do you think Jonathan made the best decision? Why?

Vocabulary

chattered	hire	milk pails
chores	jingle	missionaries

107

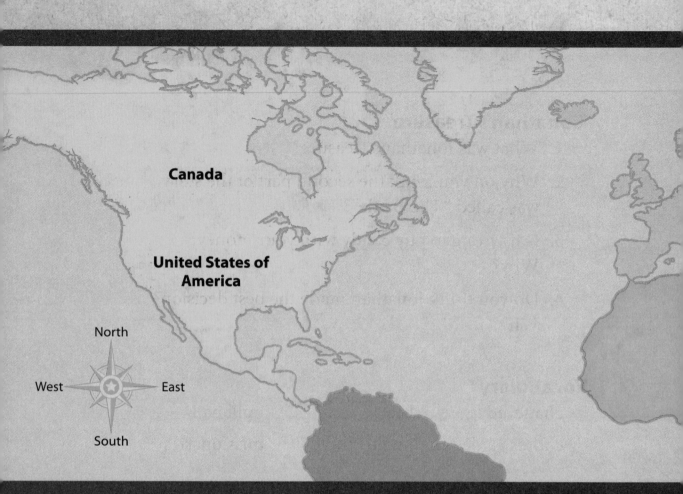

Canada

United States of
America

North

West — East

South

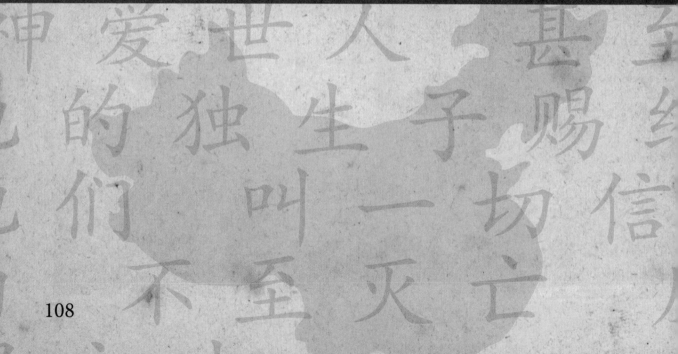

Jonathan Goforth: Missionary to China

Biography by Susan W. Young
illustrated by Lynda Slattery

China

February 10, 1859–October 8, 1936

Think as You Read

How are you like Jonathan Goforth?

How are you different from Jonathan Goforth?

Jonathan Goforth trusted Christ as his Savior when he was eighteen years old. He wanted to tell others about Christ, and in 1888 he and his wife, Rosalind, went to China as missionaries. For the next 46 years, Mr. Goforth preached God's Word to the people of China.

The Goforths had been in China only a few weeks when a fire burned their house. Almost everything they had brought from their home in Canada was lost in the fire. Only Mr. Goforth's Bible and their money were saved. This loss was very hard for his wife. Mr. Goforth reminded her that God wanted them in China. God would take care of them and meet their needs, even in China.

Mr. Goforth found it difficult to speak Chinese. Sounds in the Chinese language were not the same as English sounds. The Chinese people could not understand him.

One day Mr. Goforth told his wife that he needed God to help him soon. He said that without God's help, he would not be able to preach to the Chinese people.

That same day Mr. Goforth preached to some Chinese men. Suddenly, he could easily speak their language. He spoke so well that the men asked him to tell them more. They were able to understand all that he said.

Two months later, a letter arrived for Mr. Goforth. It told how some men had prayed for him one night. It was at the very time Mr. Goforth began to speak Chinese well. God had answered their prayers.

The Chinese people wanted to know all about these strange people from another land. Many people in China lived in paper houses and slept on mats. The Goforths lived in a wooden house and slept in a bed.

The people wanted to see the house. They wanted to see how the Goforths lived. Sometimes more than 500 people would stand outside the gate. Mr. Goforth would let them into the yard a few at a time. He told them they could see the house if they listened to him preach. The people listened and then went into the house. Many people heard about Christ this way.

When Mr. Goforth was not preaching, he would study his Bible. He loved the Word of God, and reading it was a delight. As a young child, he had been taught to read and learn verses. As an adult, he kept this habit. He got up early each day to study. During his life, Mr. Goforth read through his English Bible 73 times. He also read through his Chinese New Testament 60 times.

When he was 75, Jonathan Goforth went back to Canada. He had become blind but kept on serving God. He told the people in Canada about the work God was doing in China. Mr. Goforth had done what God had called him to do. He had told others about Christ.

John 3:16 in Chinese

神爱世人，甚至将他的独生子赐给他们，叫一切信他的，不至灭亡，反得永生。

"Jonathan Goforth: Missionary to China"

1. How are you like Jonathan Goforth?

2. How are you different from Jonathan Goforth?

3. Read the following Bible verses. Jonathan Goforth went to China to preach God's Word. Who should we tell about God?

"Go ye therefore, and teach all nations, baptizing them in the name of the Father, and of the Son, and of the Holy Ghost: Teaching them to observe all things whatsoever I have commanded you: and, lo, I am with you alway, even unto the end of the world."

Matthew 28:19–20

Vocabulary

Chinese   habit

Jonathan Goforth's Life

A. Discuss what happened in Mr. Goforth's life before he went to China, while he was there, and after he left. Look back in the biography "Jonathan Goforth: Missionary to China" to support your answers.

B. Write about these events on Worktext page 307.

Jonathan Goforth

Beginning	Before he went to China . . .
Middle	While he was in China . . .
End	After he left China . . .

Cast

Narrator	Billy's father
Chester	Billy's mother
Billy	Grandfather
Grandmother	

Little Twigs

A fable from Pocket Change
adapted for drama by Morgan Reed Persun
illustrated by Cynthia Long

Think as You Read

Are little twigs important? Why?

Act I

(Two beaver cousins playing beside a beaver dam in a small pond.)

Narrator: One afternoon two young beaver cousins were playing beside the beaver dam. Chester, the larger beaver cousin, tugged at a twig in the dam. It came out easily, and the beaver toppled over.

Chester: Five! That makes five for me! And what do you have? Only two?

Billy: Here's one! You'll have to give me extra points if I get this one.

Narrator: Billy, the smaller beaver, bit into a smooth sapling that was wedged into the dam. He pulled hard until his paws kicked up muddy water.

Chester: I'll have to help you. You're too little to work that one loose.

Billy: No! No, you don't, Cousin. You just want to take my points!

Narrator: Suddenly Grandmother Beaver appeared on the top of the dam. She did not look happy.

Grandmother: Here, now. What are you two doing?

Narrator: Grandmother tapped her tail on the logs, waiting for a reply. The two beaver cousins looked down at their paws.

Grandmother: I see little sticks floating in the water, don't I? Pulling sticks from the dam is not a game. Every piece is important. Your father and grandfather know where every log and branch is. Do you want the dam to break and the lodge to fall in around our ears?

Narrator: Chester and Billy shook their heads, but they did not look up. After a while, Grandmother went back inside.

Billy: What shall we do now?

Narrator: Chester smiled a sideways smile.

Chester: Let's try to get that twig you were working on.

Billy: No! We can't!

Chester: Come on, you little twig-tail. It won't hurt anything.

Narrator: Billy did not like to have anyone make fun of his tail, which had not grown much yet. He watched as Chester splashed into the water and began to tug at the sapling. Billy thought a minute and then joined Chester.

The two cousins got to laughing and splashing so much that soon they forgot what Grandmother had said. Together they pulled the sapling until it wiggled. They pulled a little harder, and it began to give way.

Chester: Almost!

Narrator: Then a stream of water spurted out from beside the sapling.

Billy *(eyes opened wide with surprise)*: Oh no!

Chester *(looking frightened)*: Quick! Push it back in. Hurry!

Narrator: Chester and Billy struggled against the growing stream of water. The sapling seemed to have come out easier than it was going back in. The water ran over Billy until he thought he must have gone underwater altogether. Then suddenly the water stopped.

Chester: Got it! Whew!

Narrator: Chester and Billy both examined the dam. Everything looked safe again.

Chester: Don't tell anyone about this. Not if you know what's good for you!

Narrator: Billy nodded, his eyes still wide from all the excitement.

Act II

(Lights turned low. All of the beavers asleep inside the beaver lodge. A roaring sound, like thunder, that starts softly and gets louder as the narrator speaks.)

Narrator: That night Billy woke to a terrible sound. It was louder than any thunder he had ever heard. It was a roar, and it grew louder. Billy's father rushed through the lodge.

Billy's father: Hurry! Get out! Get out!

(The roaring sound fades so that it is quiet by the time Billy's mother speaks.)

Narrator: In the dark, Billy's mother found him and pulled him with her into the pond. In a moment, they were on the bank.

Billy's mother: It's all right. We're all here. We're all safe.

(Lights are bright. Sticks are floating on the pond where the lodge had been.)

Narrator: But when the sun came up, things did not look all right. The beavers' lodge was a ruined pile of sticks. The stream swirled over and through it. The dam was gone, and there was no more pond. Billy's father and grandfather went out into the stream and moved a few logs.

Grandfather: We'll have to start over.

Narrator: Billy stole a look at his cousin. Chester whispered back to him.

Chester: Don't say a word! Not if you know what's good for you.

Narrator: All day Billy watched his father and grandfather pulling sticks and logs from the rubble. His heart felt heavier and heavier. By sundown, Billy's heart was so heavy he could hardly breathe.

When his father came to the bank that evening, Billy threw himself down by his father's side and cried.

Billy: I've done a terrible, terrible thing.

Narrator: Billy told his father how he and Chester had pulled sticks from the dam. He told how they had gone on pulling sticks, even after Grandmother had told them to stop.

Billy: We ruined the lodge. We did it, Papa.

Narrator: Billy's father picked him up.

Billy's father: It was wrong for you not to listen to Grandmother.

Narrator: The little beaver snuffled and took in a deep breath.

Billy's father: But you did not make the dam wash away. A flood from upstream came through. When that happens, there is nothing that will save a dam or a lodge.

Billy: I didn't do it? Oh, Papa!

Narrator: Then Billy cried again. He was thankful that he had chosen to do what was right. He had told his father the truth. His father kissed Billy and put him to bed on a nest of leaves. Billy slept peacefully all night.

Cousin Chester went to bed that night, too. But he did not sleep peacefully. He stayed awake all night, moaning and tossing.

Chester *(tossing in bed)***:** Ommmmmm.

Narrator: Chester knew that telling the truth was the right thing to do, but he chose not to do it. Chester did not make the right choice.

Little Twigs

1. Are the little twigs in the play important? Why?

2. Discuss little things that happen in real life, such as picking up a ball that has been left on a porch step. Why are these little things important?

3. What lesson did Billy learn?

4. Do you think that it is important for us to make right choices? Why?

5. Who was your favorite character? Why?

Vocabulary

cousins	snuffled	swirled
extra	spurted	wedged
fades	struggled	

Get Ready to Act!

Part of acting out a drama is dressing up like the character you will be. In *Little Twigs* all of the characters are beavers. A beaver is a brown, furry animal that spends most of its time in the water. It has sharp teeth to cut down trees. Then it uses the twigs and branches to build dams and lodges. A beaver also has a big tail that helps it swim.

Make a beaver mask and a beaver tail like the ones pictured below. Then use the mask and tail to act out the drama *Little Twigs*.

127

128

What Is Brown?

Poetry by Mary O'Neill
illustrated by John Wallner

Brown is the color of a country road
Back of a turtle
Back of a toad.
Brown is cinnamon
And morning toast
And the good smell of
The Sunday roast.
Brown is the color of work
And the sound of a river,
Brown is bronze and a bow
And a quiver.
Brown is the house
On the edge of town
Where wind is tearing
The shingles down.

Brown is a freckle
Brown is a mole
Brown is the earth
When you dig a hole.
Brown is hair
On many a head
Brown is chocolate
And gingerbread.
Brown is a feeling
You get inside
When wondering makes
Your mind grow wide.
Brown is a leather shoe
And a good glove——
Brown is as comfortable
As love.

Folk Music

Folk music comes from many different countries around the world. Each country has folk music that is different from the folk music in other countries. The words of the songs tell something about that country or the people who live there.

Folk music can be enjoyed by anyone. Adults teach their folk songs to their children. So the folk songs are often shared among families for many years. Folk music can be played on an instrument or sung. The dulcimer is one of the instruments that can be used to play folk music.

Granny Nell's Dulcimer

Realistic fiction by Milly Howard
illustrated by John Roberts and Cynthia Long

Think as You Read

Why is Granny Nell's dulcimer special?

The Dulcimer

For just a moment Tansy looked down at the clear water and almost lost her balance. Her thin arms waved in the air as she tried to keep from falling. Then, putting one foot in front of the other, she inched across the log.

"Whew! I thought I was going to fall in!" She let out her breath and sat down on a tree stump.

A blue jay chattered at her from a nearby tree. He seemed to be making fun of her.

"Oh, hush," Tansy said. "I know it's a small stream, but who wants to get wet!"

The bird hopped back and forth across the twig, scolding Tansy. Then he stopped, tilting his head to one side to listen. Faint music drifted down the trail.

"What's that?" Tansy whispered. She stood up and brushed off her skirt. As she crept up the trail, the music became louder. She pushed the leaves aside and stared at an old gray cabin. Tansy left her hiding place and moved quietly around the stone chimney. An old woman sat on the porch, holding an instrument on her lap. The woman plucked the strings with something that looked like a feather.

The music made Tansy think of sunshine and laughter and faraway places.

"Come here, child," said the woman.

Tansy started as though she had been dreaming.

"Well, come on up here where I can get a good look at you." The woman motioned Tansy closer.

Tansy slowly climbed the steps and stood in front of the rocker.

"You must have come up the back way," said the woman. "Not many people use that trail nowadays. Do you live around here?"

"Yes, ma'am, we just moved back here," Tansy replied.

"Folks around here call me Granny," the old woman said. The rocker creaked as she leaned back. "You must be Jim and Nora Ledford's daughter."

Tansy's eyes widened. "Tansy Ledford. How did you know?"

"I just guessed," said the woman. "You look like your mother did when she was about your age. I know your folks from way back. Ask your mother about old Granny Nell." She patted the rocker next to her. "Come and sit down."

Tansy pulled the rocker closer to Granny Nell and sat down. Granny slid a dried chicken bone up and down the strings of her instrument. With her right hand she plucked the strings with a turkey quill.

Granny played one song after another. Tansy discovered that she knew some of the tunes.

"Just watch," said Granny. She began to play a lively tune called "Turkey in the Straw." A tiny head popped out of the branches next to the porch. Then a squirrel scampered out on a limb. Tansy clapped one hand over her mouth to keep from laughing. The squirrel hopped up and down. It looked like he was keeping time with the music.

"Shhh!" warned Granny Nell. Tansy sat very still while Granny played "Pop Goes the Weasel." A flock of blue jays swooped down into the yard. They flew around the yard, diving at each other.

Tansy's eyes were bright with laughter when Granny Nell finally stopped playing. "Do they always come up when you play?" Tansy asked.

"I usually play the same time every day," Granny replied. "My little friends wouldn't know what to do without their afternoon music." She ran her fingers over the strings.

"What is that thing you're playing?" asked Tansy.

"A dulcimer," answered Granny. "An old-time dulcimer that belonged to my mother." Granny looked at the sun. "You had better be on your way before the sun sets. Come back tomorrow, and I'll show you how to play the dulcimer."

"Will you, for sure?" Tansy asked.

"Sure will," Granny replied. "Now scoot!"

Summer on Shady Mountain

All summer long Tansy climbed the back trail to Granny Nell's cabin. The noisy blue jay grew used to her visits. He no longer scolded Tansy when she ran across the log.

Tansy whistled at him happily. "Morning, Blue," she called as she hurried past his tree.

At the cabin Tansy found Granny in the kitchen making tea. "Fetch the dulcimer and take it outside, Tansy. I'll be right out," she said.

"Play 'Church in the Wildwood,' Tansy," Granny said, sitting down in the other rocker. She tapped her foot in time to the music and nodded to herself as the notes faded. "I've never had anyone learn to play the dulcimer as fast as you have. The good Lord has given you a gift, Tansy. Make sure you use your gift well."

"But the animals don't come when I play," said Tansy.

"Give them time," Granny said, smiling. "They'll come around soon enough."

"Mom says that you play at the Shady Mountain Fair," Tansy said. "She says you always win the music competition."

Granny nodded. "So far I have. The extra money helps me to pay the taxes on my land."

She looked around her at the honeysuckle vines, heavy with sweet-smelling flowers. Then she looked out across the valley to the blue-misted mountains.

"I hope I never have to leave my mountains," sighed Granny. Then she shook her head as if to clear it of gloomy thoughts. "Let's go for a walk before you go home," she said.

Tansy took many more walks with Granny Nell. Each day Granny showed her something new about life on the mountain. One day it was a pale, speckled egg from a blue jay's nest. The next day it was a tiny wildflower almost hidden under the damp leaves.

One afternoon Tansy skipped up the trail and stopped by the log to watch the rushing water. Whistling for Blue as usual, she started across the log. On the other side she stopped and looked about her. There had been no cheerful answering whistle. Puzzled, she whistled again. There was a sudden flash of blue, and the little blue jay dashed about her head. He was scolding loudly.

"What's wrong with you?" Tansy asked, ducking her head. Blue just flew up the trail, still scolding.

"All right, I'm coming!" Tansy ran to keep up with him. "Granny Nell!" she called as she ran around the corner of the cabin.

Granny Nell was sitting in her rocker. She looked up, her face white with pain. "What's wrong?" gasped Tansy, stopping to catch her breath.

"I slipped on the way to the spring," Granny explained. "I hit a rock when I fell. I think my arm is broken."

"I'll get Mom," said Tansy. "We'll bring the car back."

Mrs. Ledford was in the kitchen when Tansy ran into the house.

"What's wrong?" Mrs. Ledford asked.

"Granny's hurt!" exclaimed Tansy. "We need to take her to the doctor."

They drove over the bumpy, winding road to Granny's cabin. It took over an hour to get Granny to the clinic. Tansy and her mother waited until the doctor finished with Granny's cast.

"Now you'll stay with us for a few weeks," Mrs. Ledford said.

"Oh, no," said Granny. "I couldn't do that . . ."

"Yes you can, Granny." Mrs. Ledford smiled. "You're always welcome in our home."

"Please, Granny," Tansy pleaded.

"Oh, all right," said Granny, slowly. "If you're sure I'll not be in the way."

"You won't be!" both Tansy and her mother answered.

Mountain Melodies

The next morning Tansy balanced a breakfast tray and knocked on Granny's bedroom door.

"Come in!" called Granny.

Tansy pushed open the door.

"Let me help," said Granny, starting to get up.

"Wait, Granny," said Tansy. She walked across the room. "There, I made it!" She set the tray down, being careful not to hit Granny's cast.

"Thank you, Tansy," said Granny. She handed Tansy a piece of buttered toast. "Now you can help me eat all this."

Tansy grinned. "Mom did give you a lot, didn't she?" She reached for a slice of bacon. Her hand stopped in midair. "Granny," she said. "You can't play in the competition with a broken arm!"

"No," Granny replied. "I can't play with one hand. But we do need the dulcimer. Ask your mother if you can go get it this morning."

Tansy frowned, still thinking about the competition. "But you need the money."

"Now, child," Granny said, "you get that worried look off your face. The Lord has always provided for me. Things have a way of working out when you trust Him."

"All right, Granny," Tansy said. "I'll go ask Mom if I can go now."

"I heard," Mom said as she knocked on the door. "You run along, Tansy. I need to talk to Granny about something."

Tansy half ran, half walked up the trail. At the log she stopped and whistled for Blue.

Wings flashed in the sunlight as Blue landed on her finger.

"You've never come this close before," Tansy whispered. "You're worried about Granny Nell, too, aren't you?"

Blue chirped and flew back up the trail toward Granny's cabin.

Tansy followed. At the cabin, she took the dulcimer off its peg. As she started out the door, a tiny animal scampered out on a limb.

"You miss your music, don't you? Granny Nell didn't get to play for you yesterday."

Tansy sat on the porch steps and played the songs Granny had taught her. The squirrel hopped closer, tilting his head to one side.

"So you finally like the way I play," said Tansy. It was then that the thought came to her. "I wonder if I could enter the music competition," she said to the little squirrel. "If I win, I could give Granny the money for her taxes."

Tansy held the dulcimer close and walked back down the trail to her house.

"Mom! Granny!" Tansy called as she entered the house. She walked to Granny Nell's bedroom and stopped at the door. The two women looked up.

"I want to enter the music competition at the fair," Tansy said. "That is, if Granny will let me use her dulcimer."

"You may use the dulcimer, Tansy. But you'll need to practice a lot," Granny said.

"I will!" promised Tansy. "I'll practice every day!"

And so she did.

The Music Competition

Every day Tansy practiced playing the dulcimer. As she played and sang the old songs, Granny tapped her foot and sang along with Tansy. The day of the competition came closer and closer.

At last Tansy found herself seated on the stage with the other contestants. She clutched the dulcimer tightly on her lap. One of the fiddlers leaned over and patted Tansy's arm.

"Relax," he said. "Just think of something that you really like, and you'll do fine."

Tansy looked out across the crowd as the other contestants tuned their instruments. Then the announcer's voice rose above the noise. "And now, our first contestant is Harley Stevens, playing the fiddle."

Soon even Tansy was tapping her foot to the lively music. Each player seemed better than the one before. Then came the announcement she was dreading. "Our last contestant is Tansy Ledford. She's new to the dulcimer but was taught by the best, Granny Nell!"

Tansy rubbed her hands on her dress and walked to the front of the stage. She sat in the chair the announcer held for her. Then she drew the feather over the strings. At first the beating of her heart seemed louder than the music. Tansy closed her eyes so she would not have to see the people.

As Tansy played she thought of Blue's wings flashing in the summer sun. She thought of the sound of the rushing stream. She thought of her favorite smells—honeysuckle and Mom's home-baked bread.

As the last notes of "Amazing Grace" faded, Tansy opened her eyes. The people were quiet. Then as Tansy returned to her seat, they clapped and cheered. "Hurrah! Hurrah!"

The announcer stood up. "Everyone did a fine job," he began. As he finished his little speech, Tansy held her breath. "And the winner is—Harley Stevens!"

Slowly Tansy let out her breath and left the stage. She had not won. Dad, Mom, and Granny Nell met Tansy at the steps. Mom hugged her close. "You played beautifully, Tansy!" she said.

Harley Stevens stopped beside them. He smiled at Tansy. "You did a great job for such a young one." Then he turned to Granny. "It won't be long before she plays as well as you do, Granny Nell."

"I think so myself," Granny said proudly.

"But Granny," said Tansy, "I didn't win any money."

Granny put her good arm around Tansy. "Now don't you worry about that. Your parents want you to have more lessons on the dulcimer. And they want to pay me to be your teacher." She squeezed Tansy. "There's nothing I would like better!"

Tansy squeezed Granny back. "Me either, Granny!"

"Granny Nell's Dulcimer"

1. Why was Granny Nell's dulcimer special?

2. Do you think that "Granny Nell's Dulcimer" is a good title for the story? Why?

3. If you could choose a title for the story, what would the title be?

4. How did Tansy and her family help Granny Nell?

5. What are some things that you can do to help others?

Vocabulary

announcer	fiddlers	motioned
balance	honeysuckle	plucked
clinic	hurrah	practice
competition	instrument	provided
contestants	midair	winding

Stringed Instruments

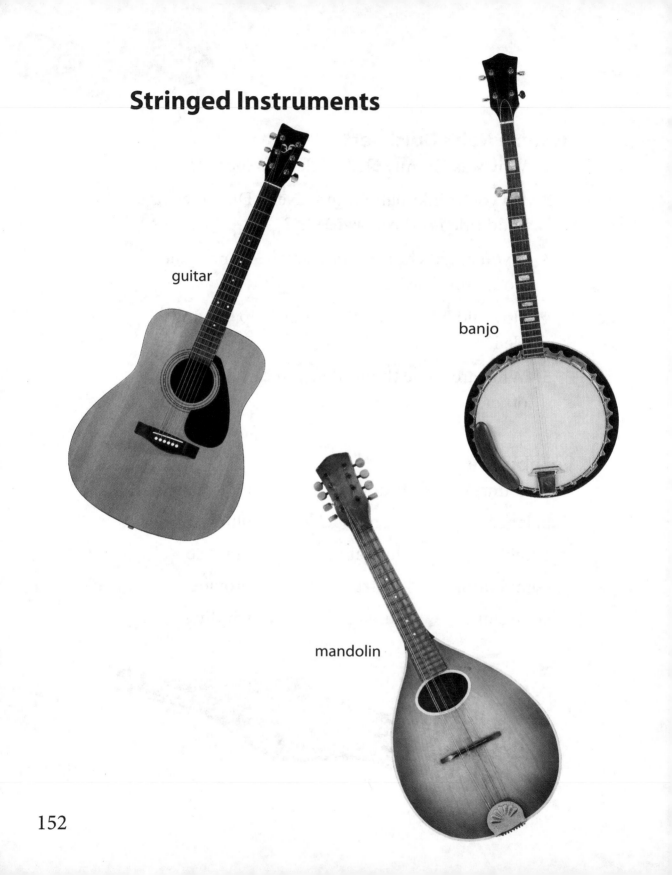

guitar

banjo

mandolin

Dulcimers

An article by Nancy Lohr

Think as You Read

What can I learn about dulcimers?

Dulcimers Come to America

The dulcimer is a stringed instrument. It has been played for hundreds of years in different countries. When people came to America in the 1700s, many of them brought their dulcimers with them. They played their old folk tunes in their new land.

What Does a Dulcimer Look Like?

There are different kinds of dulcimers. They have different shapes and sizes.

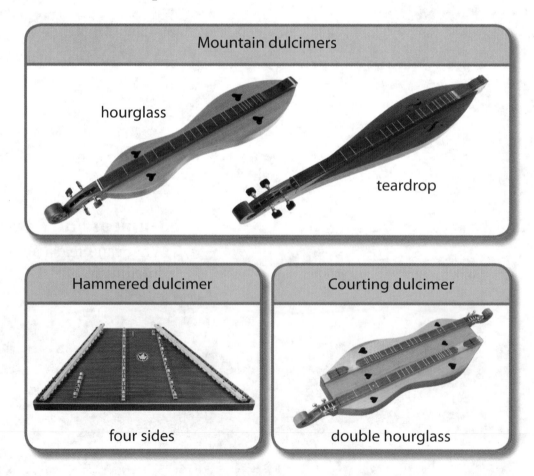

Mountain dulcimers

hourglass

teardrop

Hammered dulcimer

four sides

Courting dulcimer

double hourglass

The body of each dulcimer is made of wood. It is like a hollow wooden box. The kind of wood used to make the body of the dulcimer will change the sound of the music.

Walnut	Cherry	Spruce
sweet, mellow sound	rich sound	loud, bright sound

The top of a dulcimer has at least one sound hole. The hole can be any shape. It allows the wood to vibrate when the strings of a dulcimer are plucked or struck. These work together to make the sound.

Sound holes

round   heart   f-hole   cat

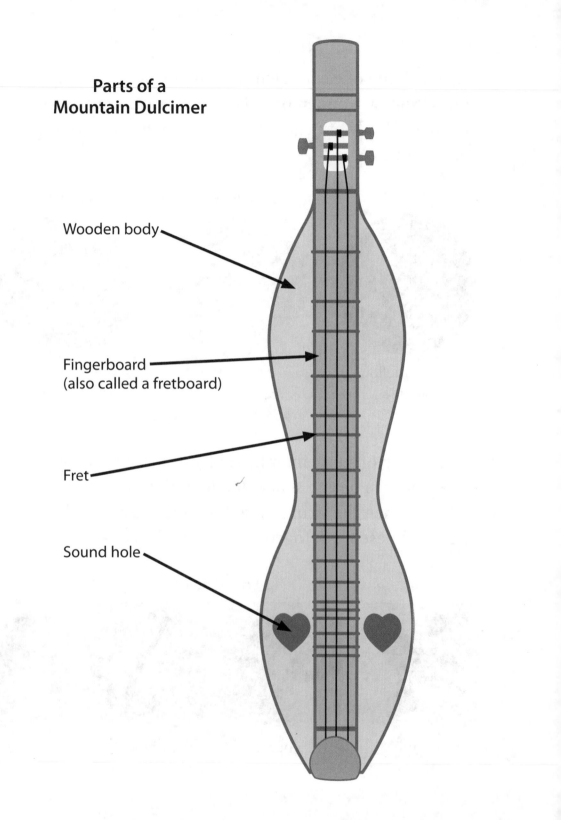

Parts of a Mountain Dulcimer

Wooden body

Fingerboard
(also called a fretboard)

Fret

Sound hole

Playing a Dulcimer

Playing a hammered dulcimer

The **hammered dulcimer** is the biggest of all the dulcimers. It has many strings that are hit with small hammers.

The **mountain dulcimer** is played while it rests on a person's lap. It can also be set on a low table.

Playing a mountain dulcimer

Playing a courting dulcimer

The **courting dulcimer** is played like a mountain dulcimer, but two people are needed to play it. The couple sits face to face with the dulcimer between them and plays a duet. Long ago a couple would learn a song together when they were courting. Then they played that song at their wedding.

It is easy to play the mountain dulcimer. The strings are stretched over a fingerboard. On the fingerboard are thin metal strips called *frets*. The frets help you to know where to place your fingers on the strings. To play a note, you press the dulcimer strings

Pressing two strings against the fingerboard of a dulcimer

against the fingerboard with your left hand. You can press the strings with your fingers or a small round stick. With your right hand you strum or pluck the strings. You can pluck the strings using your fingers or a pick.

Plucking with your fingers

Plucking with a plastic pick

The music for a simple mountain dulcimer song has fret numbers above the words. The fret numbers make it easy to play the tune using just one string on the dulcimer. First, find the fret that matches the fret number above the word in the song. Then press the string against the fret and pluck the string.

People who play the mountain dulcimer say that it is one of the easiest stringed instruments to play. Maybe one day you can learn to play "Jesus Loves Me" on a mountain dulcimer.

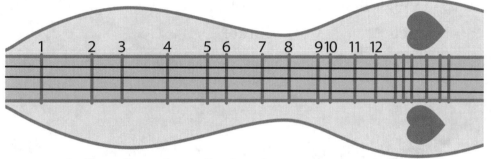

```
4 2    2    1    2 4    4
```
Jesus loves me. This I know,

```
5   5   7 5   5    4 4
```
For the Bible tells me so;

```
4 2    2   1    2   4 4
```
Little ones to Him belong;

```
5   5   4    0   2 1   0
```
They are weak, but He is strong.

A "0" means that the string is not pressed.

```
4   2 4   5    7   4   2 0    2    1
```
Yes, Jesus loves me. Yes, Jesus loves me.

```
4   2 4   5    7   5   3 0    2    1 0
```
Yes, Jesus loves me. The Bible tells me so.

"Dulcimers"

1. What does a dulcimer look like?

2. What parts of a mountain dulcimer did you learn about?

3. What can be used to play a dulcimer?

Vocabulary

courting	strum
duet	vibrate

Make a Stringed Instrument

Follow the directions to make a stringed instrument. Ask an adult to help you.

Materials: shoebox, strip of black paper (2 inches wide and the length of the shoebox), glue, 3 rubber bands, 2 small pieces of wood or 2 pencils

1. Draw lines (frets) across the strip of paper.

2. Glue the strip of paper along the middle of the top of the shoebox. This strip will be the fingerboard.

3. Cut two sound holes in the top of the shoebox, one on each side of the fingerboard.

4. Stretch the rubber bands around the shoebox so that they stretch over the fingerboard.

5. Place the 2 pieces of wood under the rubber bands, one at each end of the fingerboard. These pieces of wood will make your stringed instrument easier to play.

Psalm 33:1–3

Rejoice in the Lord, O ye righteous:
For praise is comely for the upright.
Praise the Lord with harp:
Sing unto him with the psaltery
And an instrument of ten strings.
Sing unto him a new song;
Play skilfully with a loud noise.

The Bible from Beginning to End

God made all things good, but man sinned.

Jesus rose from the dead to save people from sin.

God sent His promised Son, Jesus.

God's Promise for the Future

A Bible account taken from Revelation
illustrated by Benjamin Schipper

Think as You Read

What does God tell us about
His promise for the future?

Jesus Is
Coming
Back!

Jesus went
to live with
His Father in
heaven.

165

John Sees Jesus

Jesus died on the cross to save people from sin. Then something wonderful happened. Jesus rose from the dead!

After He rose from the dead, Jesus talked to His disciples. "All power has been given to Me. Go into all the world. Tell all people about what I have done. Tell them to turn away from their sins and believe in Me."

Then Jesus made an important promise. He said, "I will come back to earth one day. When I come back, I will make everything right."

After Jesus said these things, He went up through the clouds. He went to live with His Father in heaven.

The followers of Jesus went everywhere preaching the good news about Him. One of those followers was a man named John.

Some leaders did not want John to preach about Jesus. They arrested John and sent him to live on an island. While he was on the island, something important happened.

As John was praying one day, he heard a voice like a trumpet. John turned to see who was speaking. It was Jesus. But Jesus looked glorious! His face was like the bright shining sun. Jesus looked so wonderful and powerful that John became afraid and fell down at Jesus' feet.

Jesus told John not to be afraid. Then Jesus showed John things that will happen in the future. John saw heaven. Jesus told John to write down everything that he saw. We have the words that John wrote in the book of Revelation.

God's Judgment and the New Earth

John wrote that Jesus will return to earth, just as He said He would. When Jesus returns, God the Father wants Jesus to judge the sinful world. Jesus will judge every person who has not turned away from his sins. He will judge them, and then they will be thrown into the lake of fire.

Jesus will judge Satan too. Satan will be thrown into the lake of fire. There he will remain forever. Never again will Satan lie to God's people. Never again will he hurt them.

Next, John wrote that there will be a new heaven and a new earth. The old earth will be judged and will be gone. God will make a new earth. The new earth will be different. The new earth will have no seas or oceans. There will be no sin and wickedness. Everything will be good and right. And God will build a special city. It will be the new Jerusalem.

As John looked at the new earth, he heard a loud voice. He knew it was God, speaking from His throne.

"I will live with My people forever," God said. "Never again will people cry. Never again will they be in pain. Never again will they die. Death will be no more!"

Then an angel came to John. "Come with me," the angel said. "I will show you the people that Jesus loves. I will show you the city that God is making for them."

John describes the new Jerusalem for us. The city will be huge. It will be about 1,500 miles long, wide, and high. And it will have great, high walls. The city will be like nothing anyone has ever seen!

The new city of Jerusalem will also be beautiful. God will place many huge jewels on the great walls. And the entire city will be pure gold. The gold will be clear like glass.

There will be no church in the new Jerusalem. The people will not need a church to worship God. He will live with them in the city. The entire city will be a place for worshiping God.

There will be no sun and no moon to light the new Jerusalem. There will be no night. The light of God's glory will shine throughout the city.

Jesus Is Coming Back!

John also tells us about the inside of the city called the new Jerusalem. There will be a river that is pure and clear. The river will flow from the throne of God and from the throne of Jesus. It will flow along the street of gold.

Beside the river, there will be the tree of life. It will be a great and mighty tree. It will not be like any tree that anyone has seen before. It will grow twelve different kinds of fruit. And it will give fruit every month!

In the beginning, God had made people to rule over the earth. But sin entered the world and spoiled all that God had created.

God showed John the future that He has promised for all Christians. God's earth and God's people will be made new. All will be very good again. God's people will rule in His new world forever.

John wrote down these words that Jesus said. "I am coming back. I will judge those who do evil, but I will bless those who do good. Tell everyone that I am coming. Tell them that they need to be ready for My return."

Those who turn away from their sins and trust in Jesus will enjoy the blessings of God. They will eat from the tree of life. But those who do not repent and trust in Jesus will never enter the new city to live with Him.

Do you want to be forgiven of all your sins? Do you want to live with God forever? Turn away from your sins and trust in Jesus to save you. He will save you, and you will live forever with God.

"I am coming!" Jesus tells us all.

"Amen. Come soon, Lord Jesus!"

"God's Promise for the Future"

1. Who did God show the future to?

2. What has God promised will happen in the future?

3. Who will Jesus judge? Why will He judge them?

4. How will the new Jerusalem be like the earth now? How will it be different?

5. Who will be worshiped in heaven?

6. Who will live forever with God?

Vocabulary

entire	throne
judge	trumpet
repent	

Share God's Promises

Make a picture wheel that shows some of God's promises in the Bible from beginning to end. Follow the directions below.

1. Color the pictures on both parts of the picture wheel.

2. Cut out both parts of the picture wheel.

3. Ask your teacher to help you put the parts together.

Share God's promises with someone. As you show each picture, explain what God promised. Let the person keep the picture wheel and encourage him to read his Bible. Pray that he will trust in Jesus to forgive his sins.

USING A GLOSSARY

A **glossary** is a list of important or special words and their meanings. A glossary is found at the end of some books. Unlike a dictionary, a glossary contains only words that are used in the book.

This glossary has information about selected words in this reading book. It gives the meanings of these words that are used in some of the stories.

> The meaning of each entry word is given.

> Entry words are listed in alphabetical order.

> The syllables of an entry word are shown to help you read the word.

> A sample sentence helps you understand the word.

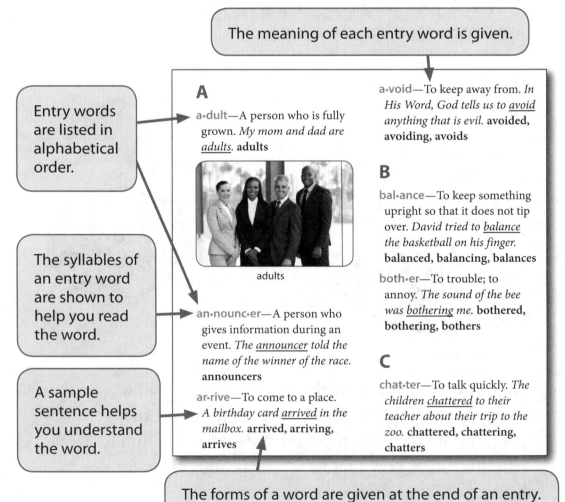

A

a·dult—A person who is fully grown. *My mom and dad are* <u>*adults*</u>. **adults**

adults

an·nounc·er—A person who gives information during an event. *The* <u>*announcer*</u> *told the name of the winner of the race.* **announcers**

ar·rive—To come to a place. *A birthday card* <u>*arrived*</u> *in the mailbox.* **arrived, arriving, arrives**

a·void—To keep away from. *In His Word, God tells us to* <u>*avoid*</u> *anything that is evil.* **avoided, avoiding, avoids**

B

bal·ance—To keep something upright so that it does not tip over. *David tried to* <u>*balance*</u> *the basketball on his finger.* **balanced, balancing, balances**

both·er—To trouble; to annoy. *The sound of the bee was* <u>*bothering*</u> *me.* **bothered, bothering, bothers**

C

chat·ter—To talk quickly. *The children* <u>*chattered*</u> *to their teacher about their trip to the zoo.* **chattered, chattering, chatters**

> The forms of a word are given at the end of an entry.

A

a·dult—A person who is fully grown. *My mom and dad are adults.* **adults**

adults

an·nounc·er—A person who gives information during an event. *The announcer told the name of the winner of the race.* **announcers**

ar·rive—To come to a place. *A birthday card arrived in the mailbox.* **arrived, arriving, arrives**

a·shamed—Feeling guilt or shame. *Asher was ashamed because he did not obey his mother.*

a·void—To keep away from. *In His Word, God tells us to avoid anything that is evil.* **avoided, avoiding, avoids**

B

bal·ance—To keep something upright so that it does not tip over. *David tried to balance the basketball on his finger.* **balanced, balancing, balances**

both·er—To trouble; to annoy. *The sound of the bee was bothering me.* **bothered, bothering, bothers**

C

chat·ter—To talk quickly. *The children chattered to their teacher about their trip to the zoo.* **chattered, chattering, chatters**

Chi·nese—Having to do with China, its people, or its language. *Jacob is learning how to speak Chinese.*

cling—To hold onto tightly or stick closely to something. *Owen had to <u>cling</u> to the handholds as he made his way up the climbing wall.* **clung, clinging, clings**

clin·ic—A place where people who are sick or hurt can be helped without staying in a hospital. *Sarah went to the <u>clinic</u> because her cold was getting worse.* **clinics**

coast—The land near the ocean. *Zoe likes to go to the <u>coast</u> and walk on the beach.* **coasts**

coil—To wrap or wind around something, forming rings or loops. *A snake was <u>coiled</u> around a branch in the tree.* **coiled, coiling, coils**

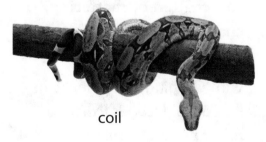

coil

com·pe·ti·tion—A contest to find out who is the best. *All of the students in second grade were in the spelling <u>competition</u>.* **competitions**

con·tes·tant—A person who takes part in a contest. *There were ten <u>contestants</u> in the football-throwing contest.* **contestants**

court—To try to win someone's love with the hope of getting married. *Sam has been <u>courting</u> Maddie for a year.* **courted, courting, courts**

cous·in—A child of one's aunt or uncle. *Abby has two <u>cousins</u> in her family.* **cousins**

D

de·light·ed—Very happy. *She was delighted with her birthday gifts.*

dif·fi·cul·ty—Something that is hard to do. *A person with a sore knee might have difficulty walking.* **difficulties**

dis·cov·er—To find out or learn something. *By reading books, Landon discovered how fishhooks were made long ago.* **discovered, discovering, discovers**

dread·ful—Causing fear. *We stayed safely in our home during the dreadful storm.* **dreaded, dreading, dreads**

du·et—Music that is written for two voices or two instruments. *Chloe and her mom sang a duet at church.* **duets**

E

eas·i·ly—In an easy way; without difficulty. *Noah easily solved all of the problems on his math test.*

ex·am·ine—To look at or check carefully. *The dentist examined my teeth.* **examined, examining, examines**

ex·cite·ment—A feeling of joy or eager interest. *We showed our excitement by cheering at the game.*

ex·tra—More than what is usual or needed. *I drank extra water because it was hot outside.*

F

fades—To disappear slowly. *The light fades when the sun goes down.* **faded, fading, fades**

faint—Not clearly heard; very quiet. *Faint music could be heard through the door.* **fainter, faintest**

fa·vor·ite—Liked the most. *Hot dogs are Ethan's favorite food.*

feath·er—One of the light parts that grow from and cover the skin of a bird. *The bird's feathers help it to fly and keep it warm.* **feathers**

feathers

fern—A type of plant that has large leaves and no flowers. *Ava saw many ferns growing in the rain forest.* **ferns**

fern

fetch—To go and get something and then bring it back. *The coach told me to fetch the baseballs from the van.* **fetched, fetching, fetches**

fid·dler—A person who plays a violin or fiddle. *Fiddlers were playing songs at the county fair.* **fiddlers**

flood—An overflow of water onto land that is usually dry. *Heavy rains caused a flood in the yard.* **floods**

flood

folks—People or one's family. *Most of Jack's folks live in the country.*

180

G

gallop—To run fast. *The horse galloped across the field.* **galloped, galloping, gallops**

glance—To look at quickly. *Finn quickly glanced at his watch for the time.* **glanced, glancing, glances**

glare—To stare at with an angry look. *Nora glared at the noisy crow.* **glared, glaring, glares**

H

habit—A usual way of acting or behaving, often without thinking. *Alex has the habit of clapping his hands when he is excited.* **habits**

hard·ly—Barely; almost not at all. *Grace could hardly see her dad walking toward her in the dark.*

heavy—1. Having more than usual. *The rosebush was heavy with roses.* 2. Sad. *Tim's heart felt heavy because he had disobeyed his mother.*

herd—A group of animals of one kind that live or stay together. *A herd of elephants walked through the jungle.* **herds**

hon·ey·suck·le—A plant with sweet-smelling yellowish, white, or pink flowers that are shaped like a tube. *The honeysuckle plants have pretty flowers.*

honeysuckle

hor·ri·ble—Causing great fear; awful. *We kept our puppy inside during the horrible storm.*

hur·rah—A shout or cheer of joy or praise. *Everyone shouted, "Hurrah!" when Grayson hit a home run.* **hurrahs**

I

im·por·tant—Meaningful; having great value. *The Bible is the most important book.*

in·stru·ment—A device used to make music. *The flute is a musical instrument.* **instruments**

instrument

J

K

L

lan·guage—The words spoken or written by a group of people. *Since Luke speaks three languages, he can talk to people in other countries.* **languages**

M

ma'am—A polite way to speak to a woman; a contraction of "madam." *"Yes ma'am, we just moved here," said Liam to his new teacher.*

met·al—A substance such as silver or gold that is usually shiny. *Copper and nickel are metals that are used to make coins.* **metals**

mid·air—A point in the middle of the air. *The hot air balloon seemed to stop in midair.*

mis·sion·ar·y—A person who tells others about Jesus and God's plan of salvation. *The missionaries went to France to tell people about God.* **missionaries**

mist—Tiny drops of water in the air that look like fog or fall as rain. *The plants were wet from the early morning mist.* **mists**

moan—A long, low sound that is usually made because of sorrow or pain. *Ruby moaned when she hurt her foot.* **moaned, moaning, moans**

mo·ment—A very short amount of time. *It takes only a moment to pick up a piece of trash.* **moments**

mo·tion—To direct someone by a movement such as a wave of the hand. *Grandma motioned with her hand for me to come closer.* **motioned, motioning, motions**

N

no long·er—Not happening anymore. *My big brother no longer plays in our treehouse.*

O

or·der—To tell or instruct. *The boy ordered his dog to lie down.* **ordered, ordering, orders**

P

pin·cer—A claw of a lobster, crab, or some insects that is used for grabbing and holding. *Crabs grab food with their pincers.* **pincers**

plain—A large area of flat land, usually without trees. *Many different kinds of animals live on the African plain.* **plains**

plain

pluck—To quickly pull and then let go. *Mary plucked the strings of her harp to play a song.* **plucked, plucking, plucks**

prac·tice—To learn or improve a skill by doing it many times. *To play the piano well, you must practice every day.* **practiced, practicing, practices**

pro·vide—To give something that is needed or wanted. *Grandma provided the turkey for our Thanksgiving dinner.* **provided, providing, provides**

Q

R

rath·er—More readily or willingly. *I would rather eat ice cream than peas.*

re·lease—To set free. *The army released the prisoners after the war.* **released, releasing, releases**

re·turn—To go back or come back. *Micah and his Dad returned home after a weekend of camping.* **returned, returning, returns**

ruin—To damage something so that it cannot be fixed. *Emma fell in the mud and ruined her white dress.* **ruined, ruining, ruins**

S

safe·ty—Freedom from harm or danger. *Dad wears a seat belt in the car for his safety.*

scam·per—To run or move quickly. *The squirrels scamper through the trees.* **scampered, scampering, scampers**

sleep·i·ly—In a sleepy or tired way. *Ella sleepily climbed into bed.*

slith·er—To move by slipping or sliding like a snake. *The snake slithers quickly through the grass.* **slithered, slithering, slithers**

snuf·fle—To breathe loudly through the nose; sniff. *William snuffled because he had a bad cold.* **snuffled, snuffling, snuffles**

spurt—To gush or squirt with liquid. *As Anna peeled her orange, juice spurted onto her face.* **spurted, spurting, spurts**

star·tle—To scare or surprise suddenly. *James was startled when his balloon burst.* **startled, startling, startles**

strug·gle—To move with difficulty. *Jackson struggled to hike through the thick mud.* **struggled, struggling, struggles**

strum—Brushing or stroking the strings of a musical instrument with one's fingers. *Mr. Scott likes to strum his banjo while we sing songs.* **strummed, strumming, strums**

suc·tion cup—A cup-shaped object that sticks to flat surfaces. *A sea star can hold tightly onto rocks using the suction cup at the end of each of its tube feet.* **suction cups**

sway—To move slowly back and forth or from side to side. *The trees swayed in the wind.* **swayed, swaying, sways**

swirl—To move, often going around and around as if in a circle. *The stream swirled over the rocks.* **swirled, swirling, swirls**

T

taught—The past tense of **teach**; to help someone learn. *I was taught to read when I was five years old.*

ter·ri·bly—1. In a way that causes fear. *The terribly loud noise scared the cat.* 2. Very. *Maddie knew that she had done something terribly wrong.*

threw—The past tense of **throw**; to send something through the air with a quick movement of the arm. *Dad threw the ball to me, and I caught it.*

tongue—The soft, movable part in the mouth that is used when tasting, swallowing, and chewing food. *The cat licked her kittens with her tongue.* **tongues**

toss—To move quickly or suddenly. *Abby tossed her head to move her hair away from her glasses.* **tossed, tossing, tosses**

U

V

val·ley—A long, narrow area of low land between mountains or hills. *We camped in a valley between two mountains.* **valleys**

vi·brate—To move back and forth very quickly. *Music is heard when the strings of an instrument vibrate.* **vibrated, vibrating, vibrates**

X

Y

Z

W

wedge—To push or squeeze into a small space. *A piece of wood was wedged under the door to keep it open.* **wedged, wedging, wedges**

whist·le—To make a high sound by blowing air through the lips or teeth. *Carlos whistled for his dog to come.* **whistled, whistling, whistles**

wind·ing—Having many curves. *Dad needed to drive slowly along the winding road.*

wor·ry—To feel uneasy or troubled. *Hannah prayed so that she would not worry about her test.* **worried, worrying, worries**

PHOTO CREDITS